D0240763

e

ef

by

W

FRANKLIN WATTS

9 1130000070206

First published in 2010 by
Franklin Watts
338 Euston Road
London
NW1 3BH

Franklin Watts Australia
Level 17/207 Kent Street
Sydney
NSW 2000

A CIP catalogue record for this book is available
from the British Library.

ISBN 978 0 7496 9416 6 (hbk)
ISBN 978 0 7496 9422 7 (pbk)

Series Editor: Jackie Hamley
Editor: Melanie Palmer
Series Advisor: Catherine Glavina
Series Designer: Peter Scoulding

Printed in China

Franklin Watts is a division of
Hachette Children's Books,
an Hachette UK company.
www.hachette.co.uk

This tale comes from West Africa. Can you find this on a map?

One day, Monkey went out shopping.

"I want to buy fish and some mangoes," he said. "What else do I need?"

"Bananas," said Anansi.
"You should buy lots of
bananas."

"Yes, I do need bananas, but I do not need your help," said Monkey.

"You always get me into trouble. Go away, Anansi!"

7

But as Monkey was busy paying, Anansi took the bananas and ran off into the woods.

Monkey was scared. Lion lived in the woods, but he had to get his bananas back, so he followed Anansi.

10

Just then Monkey
heard a cry: "Help!"

Then Anansi appeared.
"My friend Lion is stuck in
this pit. I helped you buy
your food so you should
help me rescue Lion."

"But lions eat monkeys!"
cried Monkey.

Anansi threw Monkey's
tail into the pit.

Lion grabbed the tail
with his teeth.

Anansi pulled Monkey ...

19

Monkey pulled his tail ...

And Lion was saved!
He was also hungry
and started eating
Monkey's tail.

"Help me, Anansi!"
cried Monkey.

"Lion! Aren't you going to say thank you?" asked Anansi.

"Thank you," said Lion.
As he opened his mouth,
Monkey's tail fell out.

Monkey ran off as fast as he could. Lion chased him.

Anansi took Monkey's food home. "A good morning's work," he smiled. "I do like bananas."

Puzzle 1

a

b

c

d

e

HELP!

f

Put these pictures in the correct order.
Now tell the story in your own words.
What different endings can you think of?

Puzzle 2

nervous   worried

horrible

crafty   caring

naughty

hungry   gentle

fierce

Choose the correct words for each character. Which words are incorrect? Turn over to find the answers.

Answers

Puzzle 1

The correct order is 1d, 2f, 3e, 4b, 5c, 6a

Puzzle 2

Monkey: the correct words are nervous, worried

The incorrect word is horrible

Anansi: the correct words are crafty, naughty

The incorrect word is caring

Lion: the correct words are fierce, hungry

The incorrect word is gentle